Usborne
Wipe-Clean
Seashore
Activities

Illustrated by Manuela Berti

Designed by Laura Hammonds

Written by Kirsteen Robson

Use your wipe-clean pen to do all the
activities in this fun-filled book.

6 7 8 9 10

Staying afloat

Draw over the dotted lines to see how many times each dolphin will jump. Then trace over the numbers.

Connect the two sets of numbered dots in order, to finish the boat.

Spot 3 differences between these two boats.

Draw over the dotted lines to finish the paddleboards.

On the beach

Use the pen to show Alex the way to his friends and the pool with two fish in it.

Alex

Count the starfish in each pool below, then trace over the numbers.

1

2

3

Draw over the dotted lines to
finish the three sandcastles.

Find and circle
7 crabs.

Rocky pool

Connect the
numbered dots in
order, to finish this
oystercatcher bird.

Spot 3 differences
between the two
starfish below.

Draw a line between each pair of matching shellfish on the rock.

Draw over the dotted lines to finish the three crabs.

On the water

Use the pen to show
the red boat the way
between the stone walls.

Write an X under
the kayaker that does
not match the others.

Draw over the dotted lines to finish the three boats.

Find and circle 5 more buoys, like this one.

Out at sea

Count the fish in each group,
then trace over the numbers.

5   6   7

Draw over the
dotted lines to
finish the jellyfish.

Draw over the dotted lines
to finish the dolphin.

Connect the numbered
dots in order, to finish
the turtle's shell.

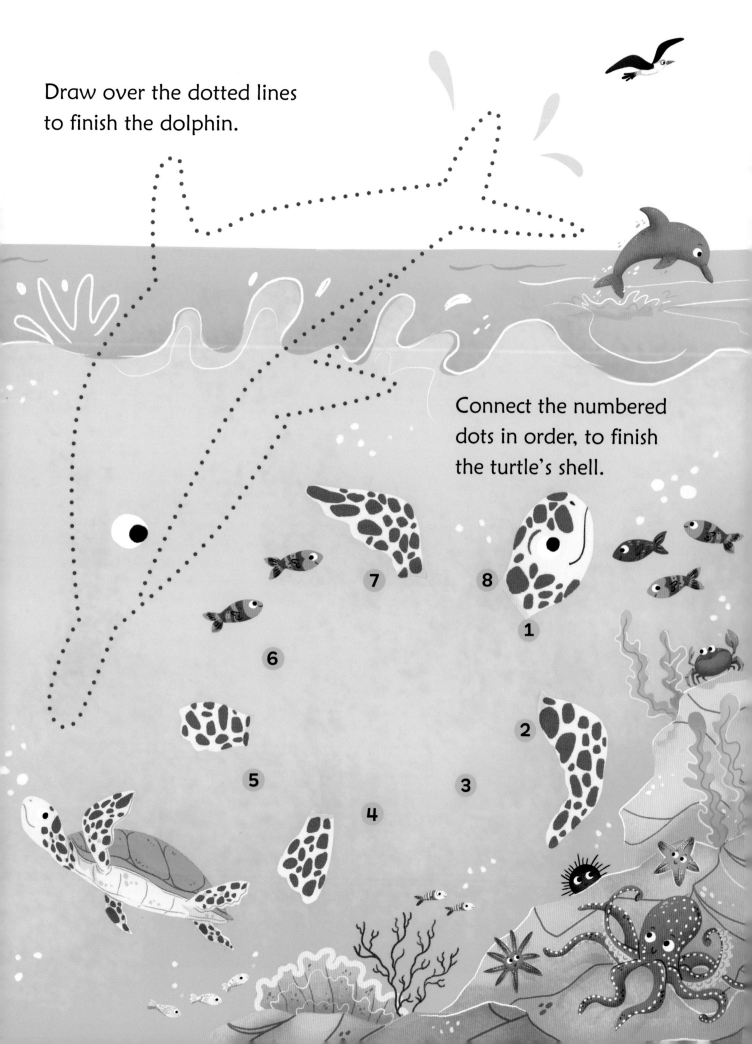

Beside the sea

Draw a line between each matching pair of boats.

Draw over the dotted lines to finish these two umbrellas.

Luca

Sabir

Spot 5 differences between the two buildings above.

Katya

Follow the trails to see who will meet Luca at the café.

Coastal campsite

Write an X under the campervan that does not match the others.

Use the pen to show Chrissy and Arlo the way to the beach.

Chrissy

Arlo

Draw over the
dotted lines to
finish the tents.

Find and circle
8 butterflies.

Riding the waves

Draw over the
dotted lines to finish
the two palm trees.

Spot 5 differences
between Layla
and Lola.

Layla

Lola

Connect the two sets of numbered dots in order, to finish the van.

Find and circle 6 sandcastles.

Draw over the dotted lines to finish the waves.

Fun and games

Follow the trails to see how
each ball will roll into its hole.

Draw over the dotted lines
to finish the sand pictures.

Draw over the dotted lines
to finish the beach huts.

Count the sandcastles,
then trace over the
correct number.

8 9 10

On the cliffs

Draw over the dotted lines to finish the gulls.

Spot 5 differences between these two puffins.